TABLE OF CONTENTS

* Full-color transparencies are found at the back of the book. Each transparency should be used to introduce the corresponding unit.

    i   Geology—Rocks and Minerals

Page 1 THE EARTH'S INTERIOR

CONCEPTS: 1. The earth's interior is made up of three main layers—crust, mantle, and core. 2. Man's knowledge of the mantle and core is based on indirect evidence.

BACKGROUND INFORMATION: The crust, about 10 to 70 km thick, is the outer layer. Soil, water, coal, petroleum, gas, rocks, and minerals are found in the crust. Granite rock makes up a large part of the crust. The mantle, about 2880 to 3200 km thick, is the middle layer. This layer is a dense rock layer of mostly olivine and basalt rock. Upper portions of the mantle are like liquid, allowing for the movement of large crustal plates. The movement of these plates causes geologic activity at their boundaries. Beneath the mantle is the inner layer called the core. The core, the center of the earth, is about 3500 km thick. Geologists believe the core is made up of a mixture of dense molten nickel (90%) and molten iron (10%). Traveling to the center of the earth, there is a steady increase in temperature. At 30 km the temperature is about 500°C; at 100 km it is 1100°C. Geologists estimate the temperature of the mantle to be about 2000°C. The core might be as high as 5000°C. It is believed that the extreme heat is present because the materials within the earth's interior are highly compressed.

When underground water becomes superheated and flows to the surface, hot springs and/or geysers are formed. Upon reaching the surface, water in hot springs may be pleasantly warm or at boiling temperatures. Surface waters usually have a high mineral content of chlorides, sulfates, and carbonates. When the water evaporates, minerals are deposited around the mouth of the hot springs, forming brightly colored mineral deposits and rock layers. The vent of a hot spring is rather straight, enabling the water to reach the surface quickly; the vent of a geyser is narrow, curved, and twisted. Water is easily trapped, superheated, and is under great pressure when it reaches the surface.

ENRICHMENT ACTIVITIES: 1. Research the discovery of the Mohorovicic discontinuity. 2. Find out about the theory of plate tectonics and movement of lithospheric plates.

ANSWER KEY:
Page 1 1. mantle 2. outer core **Study Question:** through the study of earthquakes in the interior of the earth

Page 1a 1. A. inner core B. outer core C. crust D. mantle 2. mantle and core 3. crust 4. a. igneous, sedimentary, and metamorphic rocks, and minerals b. solid iron and nickel 5. It increases. 6. a. crust b. It is the only layer exposed to atmospheric conditions. 7. a. ocean valleys b. mountains 8. mantle

Page 1b 1. magma 2. The hot water dissolves them from the rock. 3. The small tube of a geyser keeps the water from flowing out easily and allows pressure to build up. 4. volcanic 5. from minerals dissolved below the earth's surface and forced to the surface 6. steam

Page 2 MINERALS AND THEIR IDENTIFICATION

CONCEPTS: 1. Minerals are naturally occurring substances found on the earth's surface that have definite crystal structure and chemical composition. 2. Geologists use a variety of tests to identify minerals.

BACKGROUND INFORMATION: The earth's crust is composed of naturally occurring elements. The most abundant elements are oxygen (46.7%), silicon (27.7%), aluminum (8.1%), iron (5.0%), calcium (3.6%), sodium (2.8%), potassium (2.6%), and magnesium (2.0%). These eight elements make up nearly 99% of the earth's crust. Some of the elements are found as free atoms or molecules. However, most of the elements are found in naturally occurring combinations called minerals. Minerals have definite physical and chemical properties. The rocks which make up the earth's crust are made up of minerals. Many rocks contain several kinds of minerals. Certain minerals are commonly found to be the building blocks of rocks.

Six of the most common minerals on earth are feldspar, quartz, mica, hornblende, calcite, and olivine.

The identification of minerals can be accurately determined in the laboratory by chemical analysis. However, in the field it is often necessary for geologists to make identifications. They do this by observing the physical characteristics and by performing simple chemical and physical tests.

Acid Test—Diluted acid will cause carbonate minerals to effervesce.

Crystal Shape—In most minerals there are distinctive crystals. Crystals are an indication of the internal arrangement of the atoms. Some minerals do not have atoms arranged in crystals and are called amorphous.

Streak Test—Certain minerals leave a characteristic colored streak when rubbed across a piece of unglazed tile or porcelain.

Hardness Test—Minerals vary in their hardness, that is, in their ability to scratch another substance or to be scratched. The geologist Mohs devised a scale of hardness utilizing ten common minerals. Minerals can be tested for hardness by comparing their ability to scratch or be scratched by the reference minerals in the scale.

ENRICHMENT ACTIVITIES: 1. Research which minerals are most common on the earth and in the kind of rocks in which they are found. 2. Find out about common minerals in your area and how they can be identified.

Geology—Rocks and Minerals

ANSWER KEY:

Page 2 1. crystal shape and hardness 2. streak test **Study Question:** Other tests include luster, cleavage, fracture, specific gravity, and fluorescence.

Page 2a 1. See the transparency on page 2 for list of minerals. 2. Each mineral has a different color. 3. acid test and hardness test 4. a. talc b. diamond 5. galena 6. all minerals from feldspar (6) to diamond (10)

Page 2b 1. hematite, tungsten 2. chalcopyrite, gold, silver 3. a. chalcopyrite, sphalerite b. cassiterite, chalcopyrite c. cassiterite, galena, chalcopyrite 4. bauxite, cassiterite, chalcopyrite, galena, hematite, sphalerite, wolframite 5. a. U.S., Canada b. Bolivia, Zaire c. U.S., Germany d. China, Portugal

Page 3 FORMATION OF IGNEOUS ROCKS

CONCEPT: Igneous rocks are formed from hot, molten material called magma.

BACKGROUND INFORMATION: Igneous rocks are formed from molten material deep below the earth's crust. This molten material is called magma. Magma may force its way up toward the surface of the earth through cracks in the rock strata. Lava, liquid magma that reaches the earth's surface, flows from volcanoes, cools rapidly, and forms rocks with small, fine-grained crystals or glassy appearances. Some examples of glassy rock with small crystals are basalt, pumice, and obsidian. Magma that is blocked from reaching the earth's surface by rock layers above it cools slowly below the land surface. Rocks formed under these conditions have large crystals and are coarse-grained in appearance. Some examples of this kind of rock are granites, the most common of igneous rocks, gabbro, quartz, and diabase.

ENRICHMENT ACTIVITIES: 1. Find out about uses of pumice and granite. 2. Find out about growing crystals from a solution of salt, epsom salt, or sugar in water and allowing the water to evaporate.

ANSWER KEY:

Page 3 1. Igneous rocks are formed from magma; lava, magma that reaches the surface, forms small-crystal igneous rocks. Magma that does not reach the surface forms large-crystal igneous rocks. 2. Large crystal-granite, quartz; small crystal-basalt, pumice, obsidian **Study Question:** Intrusive rocks are rocks formed from magma that could not reach the surface and cooled below the surface; extrusive rocks are rocks formed from magma that reached the surface and cooled.

Page 3a 1. A. lava B. area of rapidly cooled rocks C. area of slowly cooled rocks D. magma 2. magma, heat, pressure, lava 3. G. pumice H. obsidian I. basalt 4. E. quartz F. granite 5. a. quartz b. pumice c. obsidian d. granite e. basalt

Page 4 FORMATION OF SEDIMENTARY ROCKS

CONCEPT: Nearly all sedimentary rocks, formed in layers or beds, are formed from layers of sediments that have been compressed under water for long periods of time.

BACKGROUND INFORMATION: When sediment-laden streams empty into larger bodies of water, the loss in velocity causes the larger and heavier particles to be deposited first. Smaller and lighter particles are carried away and settle farther from the mouth of the stream. The weight of the water plus the weight of the top layers press the sediment of the bottom layers tightly together. Chemicals found in the water are deposited between the particles of sediment, fill the tiny spaces, and cement and form the sediment into rock layers. Common examples of sedimentary rock include conglomerates (formed by a compressed mixture of gravel usually deposited where rivers empty into larger bodies of water), sandstone (formed by compressed sand grains), and shale (formed by compressed layers of clay, mud, and/or silt). Some kinds of sedimentary rocks are formed by sediments which include the remains of tiny plants and animals and dissolved chemicals, such as salt and calcium carbonates found in ocean water. Some examples are limestone, a very useful sedimentary rock, and gypsum. Both are formed from the remains of corals, plants, shells, and dissolved chemicals.

ENRICHMENT ACTIVITIES: 1. Find out how bituminous coal fields were formed. 2. Find out why fossils are most often found in sedimentary rock.

ANSWER KEY:

Page 4 1. Loss in water velocity causes larger and heavier particles to be deposited first; smaller and lighter particles are deposited farther away from the mouth of the stream or river. 2. gravel, sand, mud, clay, or silt, dissolved chemicals and organic sediments from remains of plant and animal life **Study Question:** Remains of microscopic marine plants and animals living millions of years ago were buried in mud and sand beneath the ocean. Under tremendous pressure and bacterial action, petroleum and gas deposits developed. When ocean water no longer covered these deposits, the petroleum and gas remained in rock-bound pools beneath the earth's surface.

Page 4a 1. A. dissolved chemicals and organic sediments B. gravel C. sand D. mud or clay 2. weight, sediments, sedimentary rocks 3. E. conglomerate F. sandstone G. shale H. limestone 4. a. sandstone b. shale c. conglomerate d. limestone

Page 5 FORMATION OF METAMORPHIC ROCKS

CONCEPTS: 1. Metamorphic rocks are formed from igneous, sedimentary, and other metamorphic rocks. 2. These rocks are changed by heat, pressure, and chemical action.

BACKGROUND INFORMATION: Within the earth's crust, rocks are subjected to pressure and heat. The weight of overlying rock strata may produce great pressures on the rocks below them. It has been estimated that rocks lying several miles under the earth's surface may have pressures of four to twelve tons per square centimeter exerted upon them. This great pressure causes a physical readjustment or alignment of the mineral particles. Pressure on rocks may also be caused by the folding of strata, as in the mountain-building process. As one goes deeper and deeper into the earth's crust, there is a corresponding increase in temperature. Temperatures around magma (liquid rock) intrusions are very high and may cause changes within the surrounding rocks. Often very hot gases and liquids associated with magma also cause a change in adjacent rocks. New elements may be added or elements may be removed. These changes can cause an alteration in the chemical composition of the rock. Metamorphic rocks are characterized by change in their texture due to recrystallization and/or their change in chemical composition.

Metamorphism can occur among igneous, sedimentary, and other metamorphic rocks. Often the original characteristics are profoundly changed. Metamorphic rocks may be more crystalline, more massive (dense), or have minerals arranged in parallel layers.

Marble Limestone changes into marble. Various impurities in the limestone give marble its characteristic color. Marble, because of its compactness, is an excellent building stone and is used for statues.

Quartzite This rock comes from sandstone. Sandstone is composed of sand particles cemented together by various other materials. When crushed, sandstone breaks around the individual particles. Quartzite, however, has particles cemented by a silica material and when crushed, the rock breaks through the particles.

Slate Sediments such as silt form the sedimentary rock, shale. When shale is subjected to metamorphism, it changes to slate. Slate is impervious to water, resistant to weathering, and easily splits into thin sections. These qualities have been utilized in its serviceability as a roofing material. Volcanic ash may metamorphose into slate.

Gneiss The various igneous granites may become changed into the rock called gneiss. It usually has a coarsely banded appearance consisting of successive dark and light bands. The dark bands may be the minerals biotite or hornblende and the light bands, the minerals quartz or feldspar.

Anthracite Coal Bituminous coal becomes hard coal, anthracite. This rock is harder and has a greater carbon content than soft coal. Anthracite coal is found in areas of mountain-building activity. Further metamorphosis may change it into graphite.

ENRICHMENT INFORMATION: 1. Research the metamorphism of slate into phyllite or schist. 2. Find out about the commercial uses of metamorphic rock.

ANSWER KEY:
Page 5 1. heat and pressure 2. folding of rocks **Study Question:** Briefly, the rock cycle begins with the formation of igneous rock which, through the processes of weathering and erosion, becomes sediments from which sedimentary rocks are formed. Igneous and sedimentary rocks subjected to heat and pressure form metamorphic rock, which may become sediments to reform into sedimentary rocks or become magma to reform into igneous rock.

Page 5a 1. A. changed by pressure B. changed by heat 2. marble—1. limestone 2. sedimentary; slate—1. shale 2. sedimentary; gneiss—1. granite 2. igneous; quartzite —1. sandstone 2. sedimentary; anthracite—1. bituminous coal 2. sedimentary 3. It has a banded appearance. 4. a. are more dense b. are less porous c. have crystals in parallel layers 5. a. quartzite b. slate c. marble

Page 6 FOLDED MOUNTAINS

CONCEPT: Some mountains are formed by the horizontal compression of rock layers. The compressional forces may be due to unequal weight of various land areas.

BACKGROUND INFORMATION: In certain areas of the world there developed in the earth's crust long troughs or depressions. These are known as geosynclines. The natural weathering of the surrounding lands caused the troughs to begin to fill with sediments. Often the geosynclines were filled with shallow seas. Marine sediments were also deposited. Centuries of deposition produced very large layers of sediment which became sedimentary rock. In some cases the layers may be several miles deep. Some geologists believe that the weight of these sediments caused horizontal compression forces which folded the adjacent rock layers. The upfolds of the rock layers are called anticlines; the downfolds are called synclines. With extensive folding of rock strata, faulting often takes place. Faults are fractures in the rock strata along which movement has taken place. The combination of folding and faulting can produce a region which has considerably higher elevation than the surrounding land—a mountain. The weathering processes cause erosion of the surface layers and often many strata are removed. Examples of mountains that show evidence of being almost completely or partially formed by folding are the Rocky Mts. and the Alps.

Geology—Rocks and Minerals

ENRICHMENT ACTIVITIES: 1. Find out about the theory of isotasy. 2. Find out and compare the ages of the Appalachian and Rocky Mountains.

ANSWER KEY:
Page 6 1. Due to tremendous horizontal pressure, rock strata are folded in wavelike patterns producing anticlines and synclines. 2. The constant forces of erosion can reduce the size and appearance of mountains by wearing away surface layers and often removing many strata of rock. **Study Question:** Large troughs or depressions in the earth's crust contain weathered material from surrounding land areas. Troughs, often under shallow seas, began to fill with sediments and marine deposits. This process continued for centuries. The weight of these deposits of sediment caused horizontal compression forces which folded adjacent rock layers and resulted in the formation of mountains.

Page 6a 1. A. area of erosion B. anticline C. syncline D. folds 2. pressure, horizontal, folded 3. a. anticline b. folds c. syncline d. Appalachian e. erosion 4. Exposed rock surfaces or core samples would reveal folded rock layers.

Page 7 BLOCK MOUNTAINS

CONCEPT: Some mountains are formed by the rising and tilting of large blocks of the earth's crust. Such movements occur along fractures in the earth's crust called faults.

BACKGROUND INFORMATION: Deep within the earth the rocks are subjected to great pressures. On the surface, the distribution of weight of land masses changes over long periods of time due to erosional forces and the redeposition of sediments. It is thought that the redistribution of surface sediments causes readjustment in the pressure forces deep within the earth's crust. The rocks respond to the stresses and strains by fracturing. This breaking may cause large blocks of rock to slip and move along the fracture. Such a fracture line along which movement occurs is called a fault. Sufficiently large blocks of rock may be thrust up and tilted and form a type of mountain known as a block mountain. Characteristics of block mountains are the steep cliffs called scarps, which are exposed at the surface. The surface along which movement may occur is called a fault surface. Mountain building by block faulting usually takes place over long periods of time. However, smaller displacements accompanied by earthquakes do occur yearly somewhere on earth. Some examples of block mountains are the Sierra Nevada and Wasatch Range in the United States.

ENRICHMENT ACTIVITIES: 1. Find out about silver at the Comstock Lode and block faulting in Nevada. 2. Find out how to tell the difference between new and old mountain ranges. List some new and old ranges.

ANSWER KEY:
Page 7 1. Rock strata deep within the earth are subjected to tremendous pressure and respond to this by fracturing, causing large blocks of rock to slip and move along the fractures or fault line. Large blocks of rocks may be thrust up and tilted to form block type mountains. 2. tilted—one scarp and one fault surface; lifted—two scarps and two fault surfaces **Study Question:** When molten rock meets impenetrable rock strata, these layers arch into a circular or oval dome. If the dome is sufficiently high in elevation, it is called a dome mountain. The Black Hills of South Dakota are an example.

Page 7a 1. A. tilted type mountain B. scarp c. fault surface D. lifted type mountain E. scarp F. scarp G. fault surface H. fault surface 2. raising, tilting, crust, fault, cracks, block 3. a. 1 b. 2 c. 5 d. 3 e. 4 4. A geologist would be able to see scarps or fault surfaces on exposed rock layers. Either or both of these are indicative of block mountains.

Page 8 VOLCANOES

CONCEPT: Volcanoes are the result of magma pushing up through cracks in the earth's crust and forming a mountain or hill of lava through which hot matter is extruded.

BACKGROUND INFORMATION: Beneath the crust of the earth is a large mass of molten, liquid rock called magma. Magma is under tremendous pressure. When a break or weak spot occurs within the earth's crust, the pressure on the magma is lessened, and the magma is pushed up to the surface through the weak spot or crack. When magma reaches the surface of the earth, it is called lava. With each eruption of hot, molten matter, a cone-shaped mountain or hill of lava gradually forms. Loud rumblings, explosions, steam, gases (some poisonous), rocks, cinders, and ashes may accompany erupting lava. The opening at the top of a volcano is called the crater. Connecting the crater and the pool of magma is the main passageway called the vent. Masses of igneous rock, intruding across the layers of the volcanic cone, are called dikes. Igneous rock layers formed by magma that had been forced into cracks and crevices of subsurface rock layers are called sills. Volcanic action not only produces igneous rocks but may also help form metamorphic rocks. Volcanoes may erupt in a "quiet" manner by spewing fountains of lava high into the air without an explosion or violence. Some volcanoes alternate between "quiet" and explosive, i.e. Stromboli, near Sicily. Active volcanoes are those that have recently erupted or those that are in the process of erupting, such as Mt. Helens in the state of Washington. Dormant volcanoes still show signs of some activity but have not erupted for some time. Extinct volcanoes show no signs of activity and have not erupted for long periods of time.

ENRICHMENT ACTIVITIES: 1. Find out about fuma- roles, calderas, volcanic bombs, and lapilli. 2. Find out about the eruption of Mt. Vesuvius in Roman times.

ANSWER KEY:

Page 8 1. Below surface—large masses of hot, molten rock called magma, under tremendous pressure, and sills; above surface—cone-shaped mountain or hill of lava, containing a vent, dikes, crater, and lava, with spewing gases, ashes, and cinders 2. Loud rumblings, explosions, steam, gases (some poisonous), rocks, ashes, cinders, and flowing, red-hot lava **Study Question**— When this volcano erupted in August 1883, it caused one of the world's worst disasters. Much of the island was blown to bits. A huge tidal wave washed over the shores of nearby islands, killing about 36,000 persons. Volcanic dust floated over this region for over a year.

Page 8a 1. A. gases, ashes, and cinders B. crater C. lava D. vent E. dike F. sill G. magma 2. magma, cooled, hot 3. a. 4 b. 8 c. 6 d. 1 e. 2 f. 9 g. 3 h. 5 i. 7

Page 8b 1. Pacific 2. a. Australia b. Greenland c. Japan and the Phillipines d. Iceland e. New Zealand 3. a. Italy b. Mexico c. Japan d. Alaska e. Indonesia f. State of Washington g. Hawaii 4. earthquakes; large land masses, sometimes just below the surface and sometimes deep within the earth, can shift, slide, or vibrate under pres- sure anywhere in the world. Volcanic areas are small areas within the much larger earthquake areas of the world.

Page 9 CAVE FORMATION

CONCEPTS: 1. Caves are formed in limestone by the dissolving action of acidic water. 2. Minerals deposited by ground water may form a variety of cavern formations.

BACKGROUND INFORMATION: A cave can be de- scribed as a hollow in the earth. It may be the result of the abrasive action of wind, of waves, or of the dis- solving action of ground water in limestone. Caves formed by ground water are the most common and are known as solution caves. Water from rain and snow seeping into the ground acquires an abundance of car- bon dioxide, generated by the action of soil bacteria. The water thus becomes a weak carbonic acid. As it trickles down through the soil, it comes in contact with fissures and joints in the limestone rock. The acidic water dissolves the rock, thereby enlarging the cavity. The action is very slow. Some caves have their origin in the Cretaceaus period. The acid water seeping through the limestone reacts with the minerals to form various carbonate compounds, which are carried in solution. As this carbonate solution enters the air-filled cavern, the mineral compounds are deposited on the ceiling. A minute ring of precipitate is left by each drop. A slender tube, a stalactite, is formed. If the carbonate solution drips onto the floor, a stalagmite may build up. Joined stalactites and stalagmites form columns.

Sinkholes are formed when the ceiling of a cavern co[l]- lapses. Some caves are formed in limestone by the slo[w] circulation of ground water below the water table. Th[e] lowering of the water table will expose the cavern to ai[r.]

ENRICHMENT ACTIVITIES: 1. Research the unusua[l] features of such caves as Mammoth Cave (Kentucky)[,] Carlsbad Caverns (New Mexico), and Luray Cavern[s] (Virginia). 2. Find out about the formation of such cav[e] features as rimstone dams, soda straws, and draperies[.]

ANSWER KEY:

Page 9 1. sinkhole 2. limestone **Study Question:** Win[d] moves rock particles which can cut hollows into sof[t] rock, and wave action can erode joints and fracture[s] on seashore cliffs into caves.

Page 9a 1. A. ground water B. sinkhole C. fissure D[.] cavern 2. stalactites, stalagmites, column 3. acidic[,] limestone, fissures 4. above 5. After a cavern has formed[,] the ceiling may not be strong enough to support the upper layers of rock and soil, causing the roof of the cave to collapse and forming a depression on the sur- face. 6. Underground outlets that drain water may be- come clogged when the cave ceiling collapses. This would allow water to accumulate in the sinkhole to form a lake.

Page 10 FORMATION OF A STREAM VALLEY

CONCEPTS: 1. Stream valleys progress through a series of stages as they are being formed. 2. Each stage, youth, maturity and old age, has its own characteristic topography.

BACKGROUND INFORMATION: The natural topogra- phy of the land surface channels the run-off water from precipitation into waterways which we call streams. As the water follows these drainage channels, the land be- comes eroded, and changes are produced on its surface. The changes produced are influenced by a number of factors—stream velocity, the underlying rock strata, the annual precipitation, and other factors. There appear to be several stages in stream formation, with each stage having its own characteristics. The stage designation is not necessarily an indication of the relative age of stream development, but rather, a classification of its appearance. YOUTH—This stage is characterized by stream valleys being narrow, steep-sided, and V-shaped. The gradient is steep and, therefore, the water is swift. The stream is thus able to carry away eroded sediments. The stream valley is relatively straight and shallow. There is no flood plain. MATURITY—In this stage the stream valley sides have a more gentle slope. The gradient is less steep and the water is less swift. Eroded sediments meander as the water takes the path of least resistance. OLD AGE—In old age the stream flows through a wide flood plain. The gradient is very low and the stream may be very sluggish. Sediments are deposited right within the river bed. The stream meanders greatly because obstacles force the slow-moving water to take various channels.

ENRICHMENT ACTIVITIES: 1. Research how oxbow lakes and deltas are formed. 2. Find out which major rivers in the United States are in the old age stage.

ANSWER KEY:
Page 10 1. wider 2. youth **Study Question:** The rock is hard and slow to erode and the land was slowly uplifted as the canyon was being dug.

Page 10a 1. A. Youth; answers will vary. B. Maturity; answers will vary. C. Old Age; answers will vary 2. a. youth b. maturity and old age c. youth d. old age 3. old age; the wide flood plain 4. flood plain 5. river bed, banks 6. a should be circled.

Page 11 EROSION

CONCEPT: 1. Erosion is the wearing away and transport of earth materials. 2. The major agents of erosion are ice, water, and wind.

BACKGROUND INFORMATION: Erosion is the wearing away of the land or carrying away the results of weathering. Erosion is carried on by water, wind, and ice. Running water is said to be the greatest of all erosive actions. As running water moves over the hardest of rocks, it can in time wear them away. It also carries with it materials resulting from weathering and deposits them into ponds, lakes, rivers, and oceans. The continuous beating of ocean waves on land, the washing up of soil and rocks, and the action of tides all help wear away seashores. Wind carries away tiny particles of soil. Dust storms are the result of the erosive power of wind. Wind can also pile up sand into dunes. Dunes are formed when something interferes with the wind, causing it to reduce its velocity and drop the particles it has been carrying. As windblown sand strikes solid rock, the abrasive action slowly wears the rock away. Such action produces rock formation like those seen in the Garden of the Gods, Colorado. As masses of ice and snow move over the land, they wear away and carry rocks, soil, and other materials with them. These materials are deposited along the side or at the end of the glacier. U-shaped valleys are examples of what the erosive action of moving ice can do.

ENRICHMENT ACTIVITIES: 1. Research the origin and deposition of loess in the midwestern part of the United States. 2. Find out how shoreline features are formed by wave action.

ANSWER KEY:
Page 11 1. ice, water, and wind 2. high mountains and polar areas **STUDY QUESTION:** The force of gravity causes rock slides and mud slides.

Page 11a 1. A. water, coastline or river B. ice, glacier C. wind, sand dunes 2. a. water b. running water and waves 3. a. wind b. running water c. waves d. ice e. wind 4. Sand can act as an abrasive and cut into soft rock. 5. by building stategically located dams and levees 6. The force of gravity causes water to move more quickly down sloping land and wash away surface soil.

Page 12 WEATHERING

CONCEPT: Weathering is the process of breaking rocks into smaller pieces by the action of ice, water, temperature changes, and chemical means.

BACKGROUND INFORMATION: The breaking down of rocks, weathering, has been and is taking place on earth constantly. There are two kinds of weathering—mechanical or physical and chemical. Mechanical weathering is the breaking down of rock into smaller pieces without any chemical changes in the rock itself. This type of action can occur in a number of ways: frost action—water seeps into cracks and pores in a rock and freezes, expands, exerts pressure within the crack or pore and causes pieces of the rock to break off; wedging of plant roots—the roots of shrubs and trees work their way into small cracks in a rock causing the rock to split and crumble; burrowing of animals—animals such as gophers and prairie dogs expose rock surfaces by their constant digging. The exposed surfaces are now subject to weathering processes. In chemical weathering, chemical changes take place in the rock, forming new products that can be carried away more easily than the original rock. Areas where water is present or the air is humid are subject to chemical weathering. One example of chemical weathering is the formation of carbonic acid. When carbon dioxide from the air dissolves in water, a weak acid, carbonic acid, is formed. This acid attacks rocks such as limestone, forming materials that dissolve in water and are carried away more easily than the original rock. Lichen growth is another form of chemical weathering. Lichen are tiny plants that grow on rocks and produce an acid that attacks the rock and helps break it into smaller pieces. Lichens use minerals from the rock to live and grow and produce the rock-breaking acid. Another example of chemical weathering is oxidation. Oxygen in the air combines directly with many minerals in rocks, forming new materials or rocks that can change into another material or type of rock which crumbles more easily than the original rock; i.e., magnetite combines with oxygen and changes into hematite, which combines with water and changes to limonite.

ENRICHMENT ACTIVITIES: 1. Find out about the process called exfoliation. 2. Find out about the five types of soil found in the continental United States.

Geology—Rocks and Minerals

ANSWER KEY:

Page 12 Rocks break down without any chemical changes in the rock itself by action of frost, freezing and melting of water, wedging of plant roots, and burrowing animals. 2. In chemical weathering a new product is formed and is more easily carried away; in mechanical or physical weathering, there is no chemical change in the rock itself. **Study Question:** Warm regions have more air humidity and water than cold regions. Carbon dioxide and moist air attack limestone, abundant lichen growth and an abundance of plant and animal decay produce acids that attack and break down rocks more readily in the warm regions than in the cold regions.

Page 12a 1. A. frost action—M B. carbonic acid result —C C. wedging of plant roots—M D. lichen growth—C E. burrowing animals—M F. oxidation—C 2. See answers to 1. 3. G. red H. yellow-brown 4. weathering, ice, water, temperature changes or chemical means 5. change

Page 12b 1. weathered rock, humus 2. rain, ice, freezing and thawing 3. humus, minerals, lichens 4. Accept any three: contour plowing, terracing, strip cropping, shelter belt 5. shelter belt, terracing 6. because erosion is constantly at work and soil is needed to grow food, which is necessary for man to survive anywhere in the world

A LAST LOOK—PART I

A. 1. Appalachians does not belong. Krakatoa and Mauna Loa are volcanoes. The Appalachians are mountains.
   2. Basalt does not belong. It is an igneous rock. Slate and marble are metamorphic rocks.
   3. Crater does not belong. Scarp and fault surface are features of block mountains. A crater is the opening of a volcano.
   4. Gneiss does not belong. It is a metamorphic rock. Hot spring and geyser are springs of heated underground water.
   5. Wide flood plain does not belong. It is a characteristic of a stream valley in the old age stage. Rapidly flowing water and steep valleys are features of a stream valley in the youth stage.
   6. Streak testing does not belong. It is a method of identifying minerals. Terracing and contour plowing are methods of soil conservation.
   7. Galena does not belong. Mantle and crust are layers of the earth's interior. Galena is a lead-gray mineral.
   8. Sill does not belong. It is a rock layer within a volcano. Column and stalagmite are formations found in caves.
   9. Syncline does not belong. It is a downward arch of rock layers. Orthorhombic and tetragonal are crystal shapes.
   10. Granite does not belong. It is an igneous rock. Limestone and shale are sedimentary rocks.

Note: These are suggested answers, each determined by a specific viewpoint. Since more than one correct answer is possible, accept any reasonable answer student can justify.

B. 1. tilted   6. earthquakes
   2. weathering   7. sinkhole
   3. soil conservation 8. Pacific
   4. old age   9. lava
   5. mantle   10. column

A LAST LOOK—PART II

A. 1. a. quartz   2. a. conglomerate
      b. igneous   b. sedimentary
   3. a. quartzite   4. a. obsidian
      b. metamorphic   b. igneous

B. 1. block mountain   2. volcano
   3. folded mountain   4. geyser
   5. cave or cavern   6. hot spring
   7. inner core   8. dome mountain

A LAST LOOK—PART III

A. 1. k   6. a
   2. f   7. c
   3. h   8. g
   4. l   9. e
   5. i   10. d

B. 1. diamond   6. block mountains
   2. fault   7. talc
   3. sedimentary   8. a metamorphic
   4. greater than   9. erosion
   5. an igneous   10. crater

A LAST LOOK—PART IV

A. The person speaking thinks that wind erosion carved the faces at Mt. Rushmore in the Black Hills of South Dakota.

B. 1. The inner core is missing.
   2. The water line is too high. A cave is formed above the water line, not below.
   3. The rock strata to the right of the fault surface should be much lower.
   4. There should be an upward thrust of magma causing the rock layers to arch.

C.
```
A N D A N T H R A C I T E I E S
B C R T U R Q U O I S E V O H G
E A O U L I M E S T O N E B T A
E L G N E I S S H A L L G S J L
L C P I G R F H L A P Y R I T E
W I O S L A E T A P P A D O N A
O T F I L D O S L A T Y I I Z I
L E G O N E J M M D I E A A I D
I X Y S W N O A E A S Y T N R C
V Z O O H A A R T R O P E U C A
I Q G R T A B E E A M A N O P P
K I K U L L A H J T O R N A A T
E R P U M I C E J R W O E X I T
N U S A N D S T O N E P I E H I
D S U L F U R P K V B A S A L T
O P M L P D Q U A R T Z O U C E
```

The following section contains the student worksheets. Each worksheet should be introduced by the corresponding transparency found at the back of this book.

The Earth's Interior

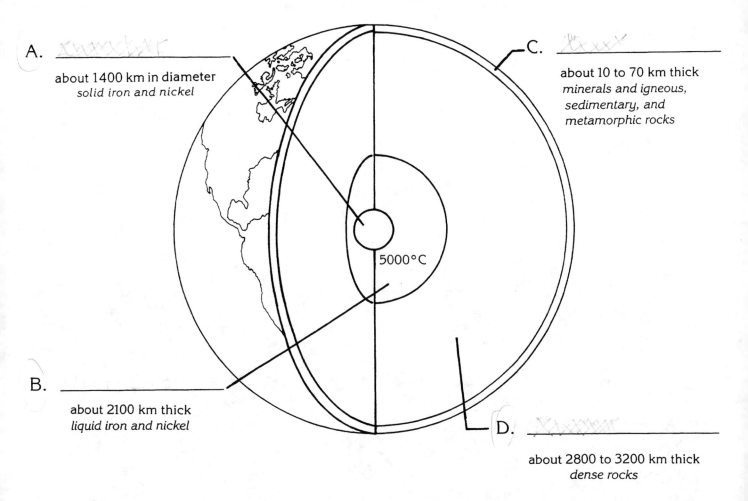

A. _____
about 1400 km in diameter
solid iron and nickel

C. _____
about 10 to 70 km thick
*minerals and igneous,
sedimentary, and
metamorphic rocks*

5000°C

B. _____
about 2100 km thick
liquid iron and nickel

D. _____
about 2800 to 3200 km thick
dense rocks

1. Label the layers of the earth on lines A—D.

2. Which layers can only be studied by indirect means? _____

3. Which layer contains the highest mountains and the deepest oceans? _____

4. What is the composition of:

   a. the outermost layer of the earth? _____

   b. the innermost layer? _____

5. What happens to the temperature of the rocks as the layers go deeper into the earth? _____
_____

6. a. In which layer does erosion take place? _____

   b. Why? _____

7. a. In what areas is the outermost layer of the earth the thinnest? _____

   b. Where is it the thickest? _____

8. Which layer has the greatest mass? _____

Hot Springs and Geysers

Hot springs and *geysers* are underground waters heated by magma or gases.

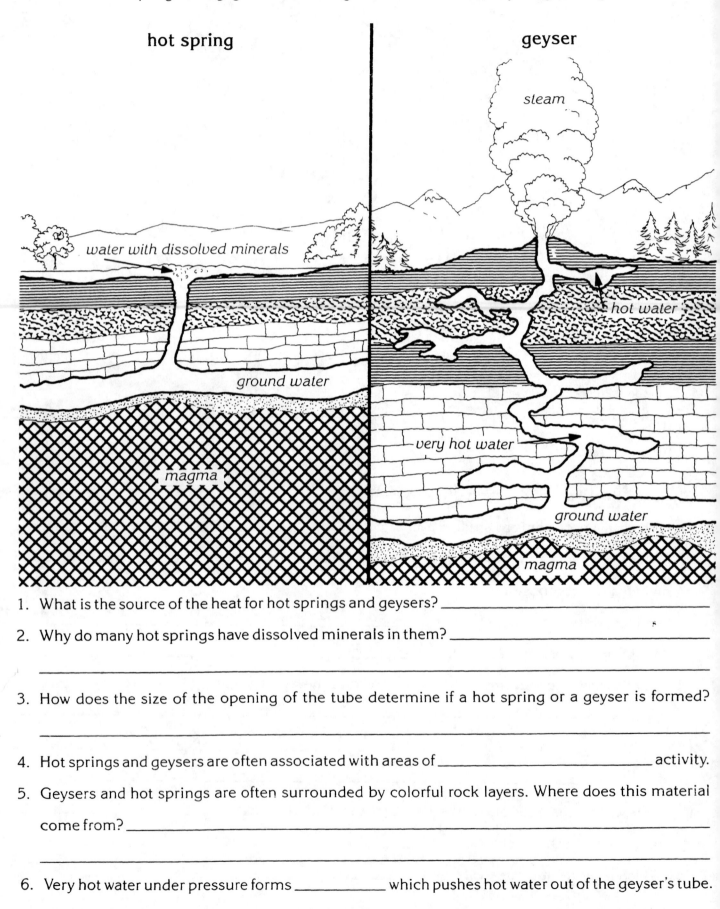

1. What is the source of the heat for hot springs and geysers? _____

2. Why do many hot springs have dissolved minerals in them? _____

   _____

3. How does the size of the opening of the tube determine if a hot spring or a geyser is formed?

   _____

4. Hot springs and geysers are often associated with areas of _____ activity.

5. Geysers and hot springs are often surrounded by colorful rock layers. Where does this material

   come from? _____

   _____

6. Very hot water under pressure forms _____ which pushes hot water out of the geyser's tube.

Minerals and Their Identification

Minerals are natural substances that have definite crystal structure and chemical composition.

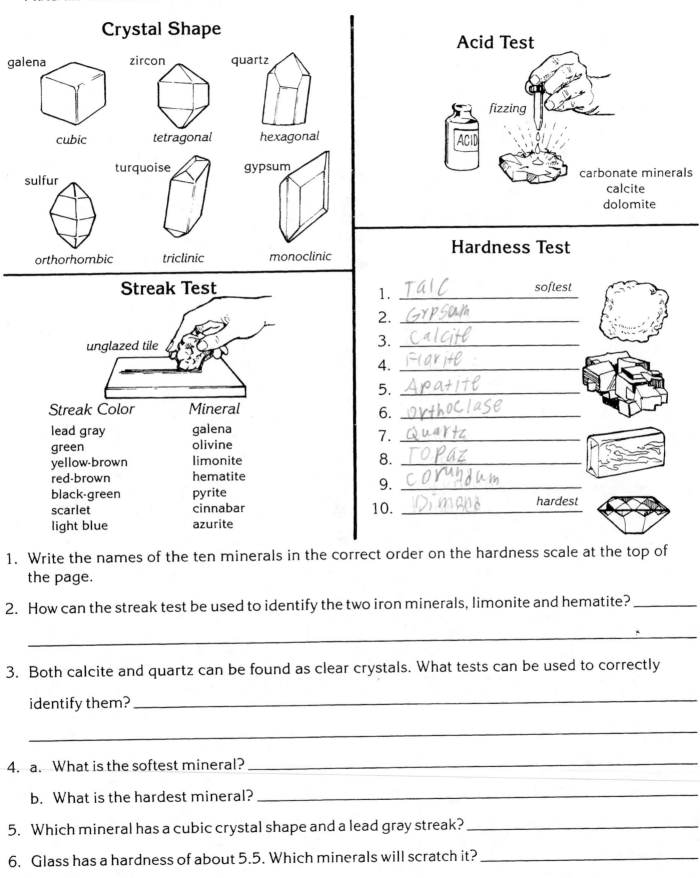

Crystal Shape

galena — cubic
zircon — tetragonal
quartz — hexagonal
sulfur — orthorhombic
turquoise — triclinic
gypsum — monoclinic

Acid Test

fizzing

ACID

carbonate minerals
calcite
dolomite

Hardness Test

1. Talc   *softest*
2. Gypsum
3. Calcite
4. Fluorite
5. Apatite
6. Orthoclase
7. Quartz
8. Topaz
9. Corundum
10. Dimond   *hardest*

Streak Test

unglazed tile

Streak Color	Mineral
lead gray	galena
green	olivine
yellow-brown	limonite
red-brown	hematite
black-green	pyrite
scarlet	cinnabar
light blue	azurite

1. Write the names of the ten minerals in the correct order on the hardness scale at the top of the page.

2. How can the streak test be used to identify the two iron minerals, limonite and hematite? _____
_____

3. Both calcite and quartz can be found as clear crystals. What tests can be used to correctly identify them? _____
_____

4. a. What is the softest mineral? _____

   b. What is the hardest mineral? _____

5. Which mineral has a cubic crystal shape and a lead gray streak? _____

6. Glass has a hardness of about 5.5. Which minerals will scratch it? _____
_____

Ores

An *ore* is a rock or mineral that has sufficient quantity of a metal to be extracted commercially.

Name of Ore	Metal Component	Uses
bauxite *Jamaica, Australia* ∗	aluminum	cookware aircraft
cassiterite · *Bolivia, Zaire*∗	tin	metal coatings, bronze and pewter
chalcopyrite *United States, Canada* ∗	copper	wire, coins, bronze, brass, pewter
galena *Germany, United States*∗	lead	pipes, batteries, pewter
gold *South Africa, USSR* ∗	gold	jewelry, coins
hematite *United States, Brazil*∗	iron	steel for automobiles and buildings
pitchblende *Zaire, Canada* ∗	uranium	nuclear fuel
silver *Norway, United States*∗	silver	jewelry, coins
sphalerite *United States, Germany*∗	zinc	galvanized iron, brass
wolframite *China, Portugal* ∗	tungsten	light bulb filaments, steels

∗ *Major ore-producing countries*

1. Which ores are used in making various kinds of steel? _____

2. Which ores contain metals used in making coins? _____

3. Name the ores which contain metals for each of these alloys:

   a. brass _____

   b. bronze _____

   c. pewter _____

4. Which ores are sources of metals used in the making of automobiles? _____

   _____

5. A light bulb contains the metals listed below. From which country might each one come?

   a. copper _____   c. zinc _____

   b. tin _____   d. tungsten _____

Formation of Igneous Rocks

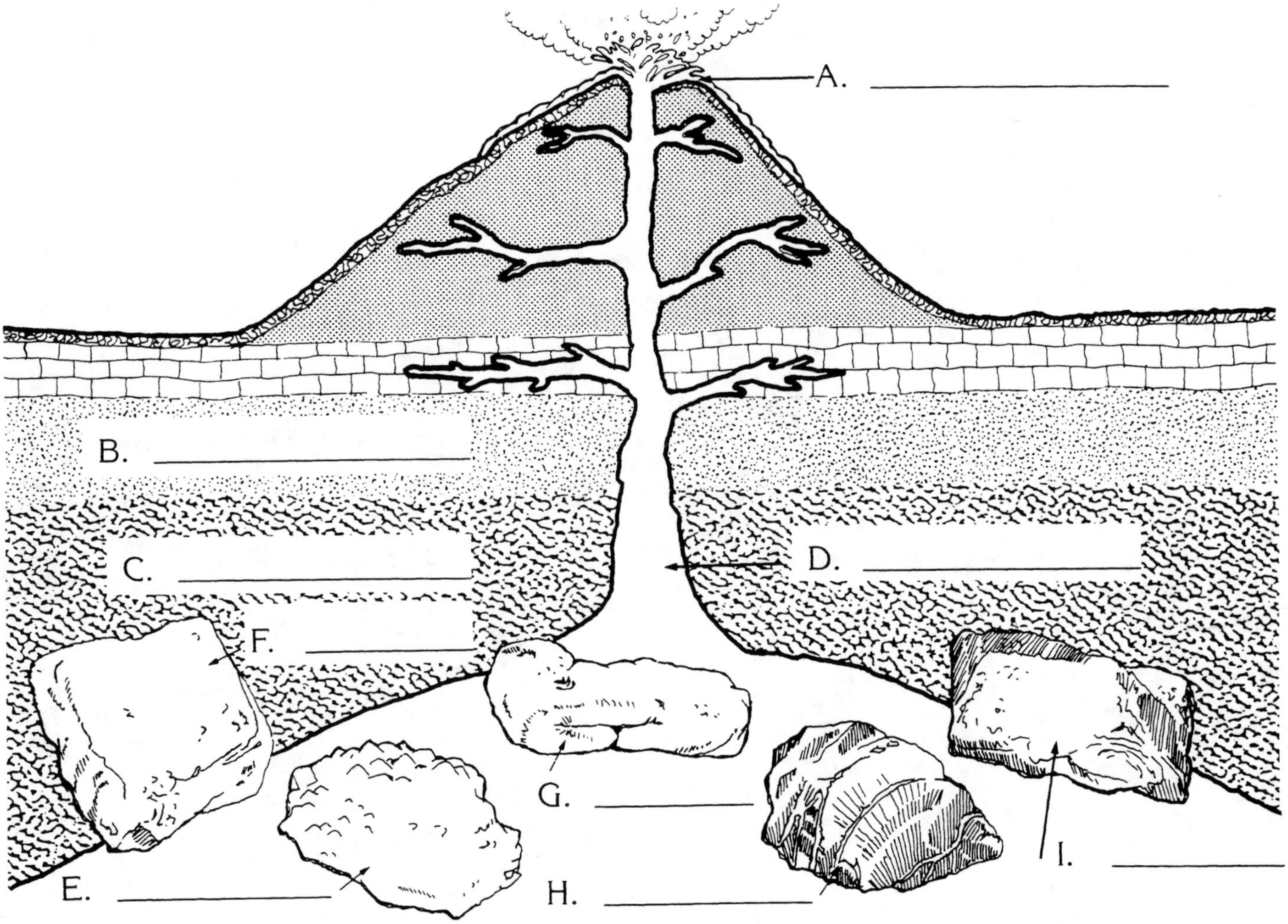

A. _____

B. _____

C. _____

D. _____

F. _____

E. _____

G. _____

H. _____

I. _____

1. Locate and label on lines A, B, C, and D: area of slowly cooled rocks, area of rapidly cooled rocks, lava, magma.

2. When hot molten rock called _____ is forced upward by _____ and _____ , it reaches the surface and is called _____ .

3. Locate and label these small crystal rocks: pumice, basalt, and obsidian.

4. Locate and label these large crystal rocks: quartz and granite.

5. Write the name of the rock in Column B before its description in Column A.

Column A	Column B
_____ a. glass-like large crystals	granite
_____ b. sponge-like appearance	pumice
_____ c. looks like smooth glass	basalt
_____ d. large crystal rock with mixed minerals	obsidian
_____ e. small crystal rock, usually dark in color	quartz

Formation of Sedimentary Rocks

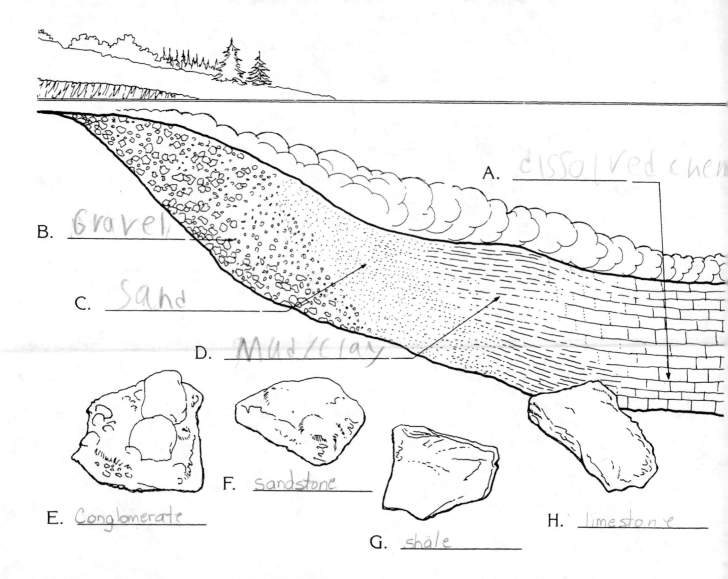

A. _dissolved chem_

B. _Gravel_

C. _Sand_

D. _Mud/clay_

E. _Conglomerate_

F. _sandstone_

G. _shale_

H. _limestone_

1. Locate and label on lines A-D the following sediments deposited by rivers: mud or clay; sand; gravel; dissolved chemicals and organic sediments.

2. Fill in the missing words: The ___weight___ of water and the top layer of ___sediments___ press the bottom layers tightly together to form ___sedimentary___ rocks.

3. Locate and label on lines E-H the following rocks: sandstone, conglomerate, limestone, shale.

4. Write the name of the rock in Column B on the line before its description in Column A.

	Column A	Column B
a. _sandstone_	has a gritty feeling	conglomerate
b. _shale_	formed by mud or clay under pressure	shale
c. _conglomerate_	a mixture of different-sized sediments	limestone
d. _limestone_	composed of the mineral calcite	sandstone

Formation of Metamorphic Rocks

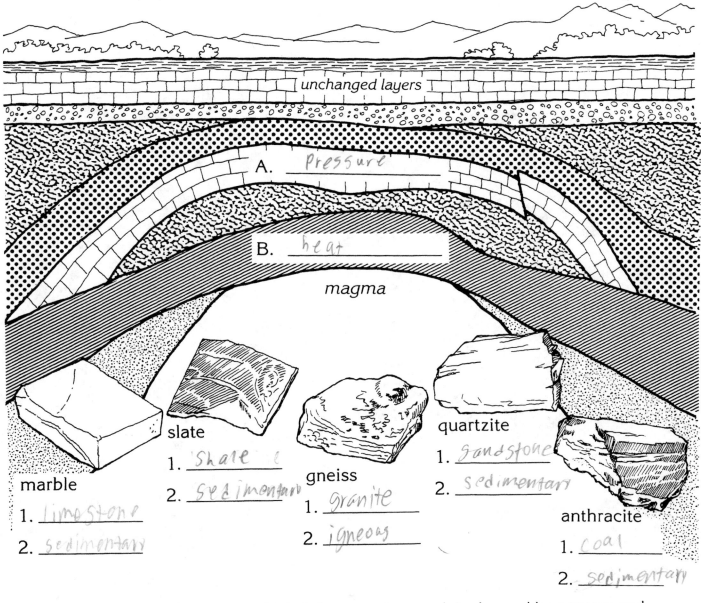

unchanged layers

A. _Pressure_

B. _heat_

magma

marble
1. _limestone_
2. _sedimentary_

slate
1. _shale_
2. _sedimentary_

gneiss
1. _granite_
2. _igneous_

quartzite
1. _sandstone_
2. _sedimentary_

anthracite
1. _coal_
2. _sedimentary_

1. In the drawing above, locate and label the area where rock is changed by pressure and the area where it is changed by heat.

2. On line 1 under each picture of a metamorphic rock, write the name of the original rock from which it was formed. On line 2 write igneous if the original rock was an igneous rock; write sedimentary if the original was sedimentary.

3. How does gneiss differ from the rock from which it was formed? _gneiss has a_ _banded appearance_

4. Place a check before each phrase that would make this sentence a correct statement. Rocks that are changed by metamorphism
   a. _✓_ are more dense.   _____ are less dense.
   b. _____ are more porous.   _✓_ are less porous.
   c. _✓_ have crystals in parallel layers.   _____ have crystals in nonparallel layers.

5. What type of metamorphic rock could be produced from each of these materials?
   a. sand _quartzite_   b. mud _slate_   c. lime _marble_

Geology—Rocks and Minerals 5a.

Folded Mountains

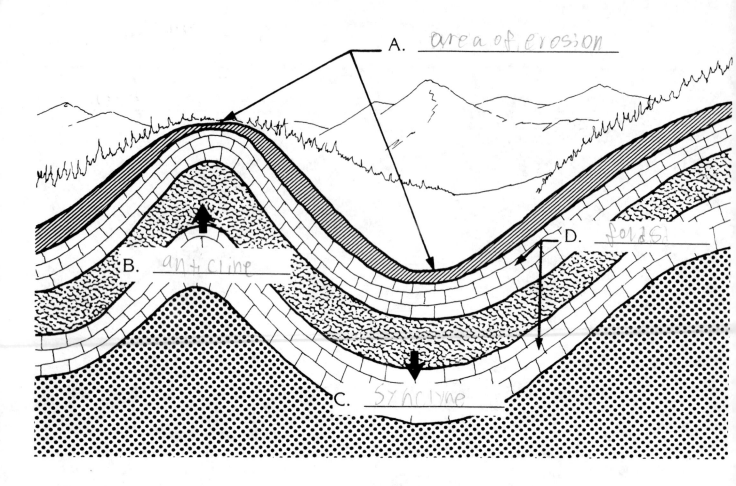

A. _area of erosion_

B. _anticline_

C. _syncline_

D. _folds_

1. In the drawing above, locate and label each of the following:
   anticline   folds   syncline   area of erosion

2. Fill in the missing words: Due to great _pressure_ on rock layers, _horizontal_

   pressure is put on these layers to form _folded_ mountains.

3. Write the word from Column B on the line before its description in Column A.

Column A		Column B
anticline a. upfold of rock layers		Appalachian
2 _folds_ b. wavy layers of rock		erosion
syncline c. downfold of rock layers		syncline
4 _Appalachian_ d. example of folded mountains		anticline
1 _erosion_ e. removes and changes rock layers		folds

4. Describe the way a geologist can tell if a mountain chain was formed by the folding of rock

   layers. _exposed rock layers or core samples_ _____

   _____

Block Mountains

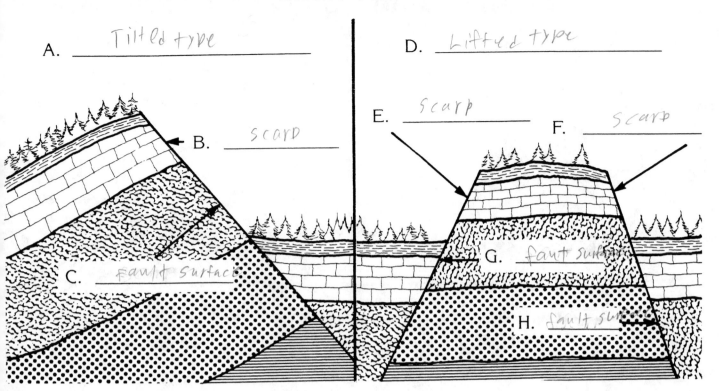

A. ___Tilted type___

B. ___scarp___

C. ___fault surface___

D. ___Lifted type___

E. ___scarp___

F. ___scarp___

G. ___fault surface___

H. ___fault surface___

1. Locate and label on lines A-H the following:

   lifted type mountain   scarps   fault surfaces   tilted type mountain

2. Fill in the missing words: Due to the ___raising___ and ___tilting___ of large
   blocks of the earth's ___crust___ along ___fault___ lines, which are
   ___cracks___ or breaks in rock layers, ___block___ mountains are formed.

3. Write the number of the word in Column B on the line before its description in Column A.

   ### Column A

   ___scarp___ a. steep mountain face

   ___tilted type___ b. mountain type with one steep face

   ___fault___ c. a fracture line in rock strata

   ___Alps___ d. example of block mountains

   ___lifted type___ e. mountain type with two steep faces

   ### Column B

   1. scarp

   2. tilted type

   3. Alps

   4. lifted type

   5. fault

4. Describe the way a geologist can tell if a mountain chain was formed by the faulting of large
   blocks. ___They can tell if there exposed rock layers on wich to see___
   ___scarps or fant surfaces___

Geology—Rocks and Minerals   7a.

Volcanoes and Dome Mountains

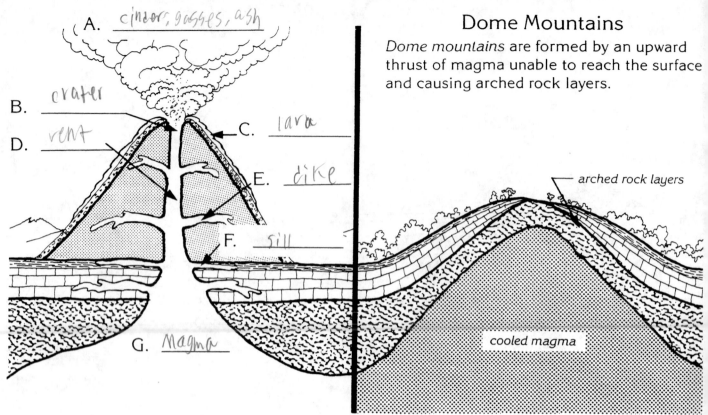

A. _cinders, gasses, ash_

B. _crater_

D. _vent_

C. _lava_

E. _dike_

F. _sill_

G. _Magma_

Dome Mountains

Dome mountains are formed by an upward thrust of magma unable to reach the surface and causing arched rock layers.

arched rock layers

cooled magma

1. Locate and label on lines A-G these parts of a volcano:

   vent   sill   magma   dike   crater   gases, ashes, and cinders   lava

2. Fill in the missing words: _____Magma_____ is common to both volcanoes and domed mountains. In domed mountains it is _____cooled_____ ; in volcanoes it is very, very _____hot_____ .

3. Write the number of the item in Column B on the line before its description in Column A.

Column A		Column B
magma	a. molten rock deep within the earth	1. lava
crater	b. opening of a volcano	2. vent
sill	c. magma flow below surface of volcano	3. gases, ashes, cinders
lava	d. magma that reaches surface	4. magma
vent	e. connects pool of magma to crater	5. Mt. St. Helens
_9_	f. example of dome mountains in USA	6. sill
_3_	g. spewed into atmosphere during volcanic eruption	7. dike
_5_	h. an active American volcano	8. crater
dike	i. magma flow across layers of volcanic cone	9. Black Hills of South Dakota

Volcano and Earthquake Areas

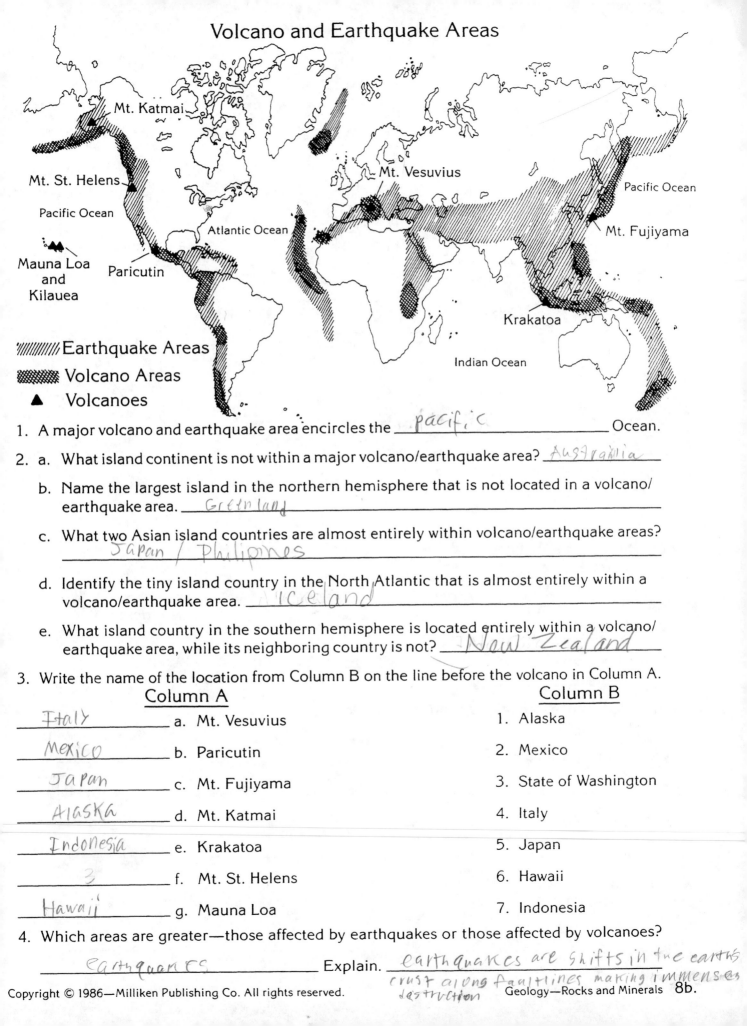

Mt. Katmai

Mt. St. Helens

Pacific Ocean

Mauna Loa and Kilauea

Paricutin

Atlantic Ocean

Mt. Vesuvius

Pacific Ocean

Mt. Fujiyama

Krakatoa

Indian Ocean

////// Earthquake Areas

▨▨ Volcano Areas

▲ Volcanoes

1. A major volcano and earthquake area encircles the ___pacific___ Ocean.

2. a. What island continent is not within a major volcano/earthquake area? ___Australlia___

   b. Name the largest island in the northern hemisphere that is not located in a volcano/earthquake area. ___Greenland___

   c. What two Asian island countries are almost entirely within volcano/earthquake areas?
      ___Japan / Philipines___

   d. Identify the tiny island country in the North Atlantic that is almost entirely within a volcano/earthquake area. ___Iceland___

   e. What island country in the southern hemisphere is located entirely within a volcano/earthquake area, while its neighboring country is not? ___New Zealand___

3. Write the name of the location from Column B on the line before the volcano in Column A.

Column A		Column B
___Italy___ a. Mt. Vesuvius		1. Alaska
___Mexico___ b. Paricutin		2. Mexico
___Japan___ c. Mt. Fujiyama		3. State of Washington
___Alaska___ d. Mt. Katmai		4. Italy
___Indonesia___ e. Krakatoa		5. Japan
___3___ f. Mt. St. Helens		6. Hawaii
___Hawaii___ g. Mauna Loa		7. Indonesia

4. Which areas are greater—those affected by earthquakes or those affected by volcanoes?
   ___earthquakes___ Explain. ___earthquakes are shifts in the earths crust along faultlines making immenses destruction___

Geology—Rocks and Minerals **8b.**

Cave Formation

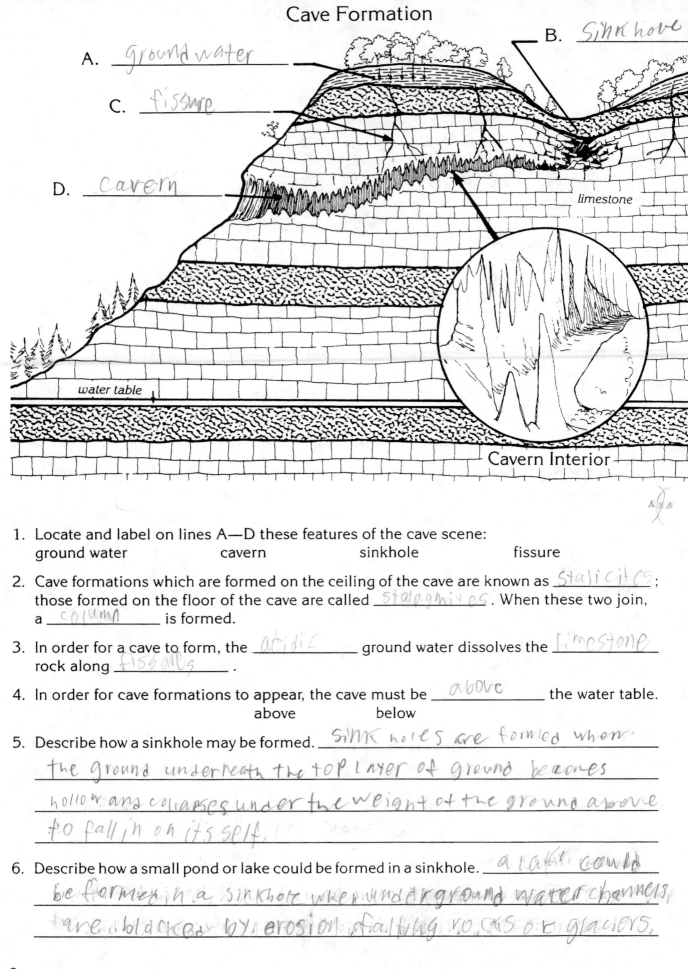

A. _ground water_

B. _sinkhole_

C. _fissure_

D. _cavern_

limestone

water table

Cavern Interior

1. Locate and label on lines A—D these features of the cave scene:
   ground water   cavern   sinkhole   fissure

2. Cave formations which are formed on the ceiling of the cave are known as _stalicites_; those formed on the floor of the cave are called _stalagmites_. When these two join, a _column_ is formed.

3. In order for a cave to form, the _acidic_ ground water dissolves the _limestone_ rock along _fissures_ .

4. In order for cave formations to appear, the cave must be _above_ the water table.
   above   below

5. Describe how a sinkhole may be formed. _Sink holes are formed when the ground underneath the top layer of ground becomes hollow and collapses under the weight of the ground above to fall in on it's self._

6. Describe how a small pond or lake could be formed in a sinkhole. _a lake could be formed in a sinkhole when underground water channels are blocked by erosion, falling rocks or glaciers._

Formation of a Stream Valley

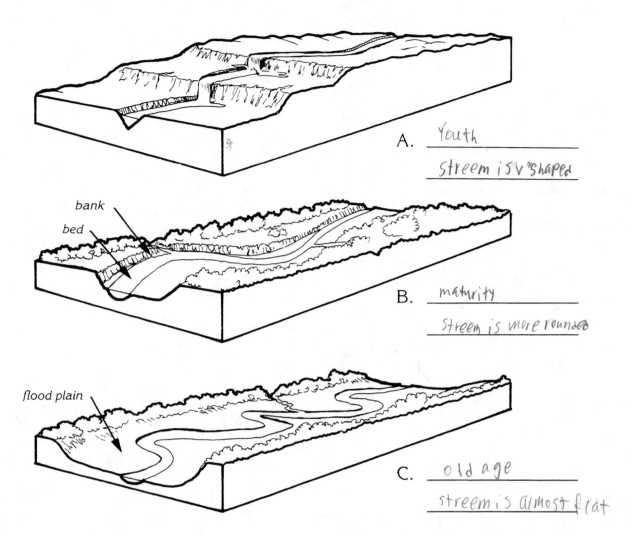

A. __Youth__
   __Streem is v"shaped__

B. __maturity__
   __Streem is more rounded__

C. __old age__
   __streem is almost flat__

bank
bed
flood plain

1. On lines A-C name each stage of stream development. Then write one characteristic of that stage.

2. Which stage is most likely to have each of these features?

   a. waterfalls ___youth___   c. rapids ___youth___

   b. wide valleys ___old age and maturity___   d. deltas ___old age___

3. At what stage is the Mississippi River? ___old age___ What is the evidence? ___wide___
   ___flood plain and the streem menders___

4. The area where flood waters deposit the silt and rocks is known as the ___flood plane___ .

5. The channel of a river is called its ___bed___ and the sides are called ___bank___ .

6. Circle the profile that best represents that of a river still actively eroding its channel.

   a.   (b.)   c.

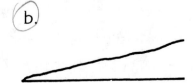

Geology—Rocks and Minerals **10a.**

Erosion

Erosion is the continuous wearing away of land by wind, water, and ice.

A. _water (waves)_
cliffs, caves

B. _Ice_
river vallers

C. _wind_
desert platformes

1. On lines A, B, and C write in the names of the three agents of erosion. Then name a geological feature associated with each type.

2. a. Which agent is responsible for most erosion action? _water_

   b. Name the two major kinds of this type of erosion action. _waves, rivers_

3. Which erosional agent is responsible for each of these geological features?

   a. Garden of the Gods, Colorado _____

   b. Mississippi River delta _water_

   c. Florida ocean beaches _water_

   d. glacier valleys _____

   e. dunes in White Sands National Park, New Mexico _wind_

4. Describe how blowing sand can cause erosion. _The sand in the wind rubs_ _aginst the eroding object speejing up the prosess_

5. How can erosion by flooding water be prevented? _by building dam_

   _____

6. Explain why sloping land erodes more easily than flat land. _it slides fast because_ _the erosin agent will go faster with more vel._ _(gravity)_

Weathering

A. _frost action (M)_   B. _carbonic acid (C) result_   C. _wedging of plant roots (M)_

D. _lichen growth (C)_   E. _burrowing (M)_

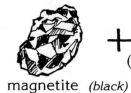 $+$ O (oxygen) $=$ $+$ H$_2$O (water) $=$

magnetite *(black)*   hematite   limonite

F. _oxidation_   G. (_red_)   H. (_yellow-brown_)

1. Locate and label on lines A—F the following weathering processes:
   wedging of plant roots   lichen growth   frost action   oxidation
   burrowing animals   carbonic acid result

2. On lines A—F, after each process write <u>M</u> if the process is mechanical weathering or <u>C</u> if it is chemical weathering.

3. On lines G and H write in the color of the oxidized rocks.

4. Fill in the missing words: The breaking of rocks into smaller pieces is called
   weathering . Three natural forces that can cause the breaking of rocks into smaller
   pieces are _water_ , _ice_ , and _chemical change, temp change_

5. A rock begins to _change_ as soon as it is exposed to the weather.

Geology—Rocks and Minerals **12a.**

Soil

Soil, composed of weathered rock and humus, is the material on the earth's crust that supports plants.

Rain, ice, thawing, and freezing break down rocks and some mineral particles.

Simple plants and animals begin to live on weathered rock.

Lichens produce acid; organisms die and deposit organic matter (humus).

Top layer of soil is formed and is able to support plant roots.

Cover of vegetation is formed; soil contains minerals.

Soil conservation is essential for man's survival today and in the future.

Ways to Conserve Soil

Contour plowing

Cultivated rows run sideways, rather than up and down, on hillsides. This slows down the water as it flows down hillsides.

Terracing

Step-like ridges are built, arranged sideways on a hill. This holds and slows down water and soil being carried away.

Strip cropping

Different crops are grown on the same piece of land. A large area of corn grows next to a large area of ground cover (alfalfa). The next year the crops grown in these areas are reversed. The ground cover crop catches and holds any soil washed away from the other crop.

Shelter belt

Rows of trees are planted close together to help force wind movement upward, away from the ground.

1. Soil is made of ___weathered rock___ and ___humus___

2. Name three weathering forces that help change rocks into soil. ___ice, rain, freezing and___

3. Fill in the missing words: The remains of dead plants and other organisms are called ___humus___ . Plants grow well in soil containing a rich supply of ___minerals___ . Simple plants that produce a rock-breaking acid are called ___lichens___ .

4. Name three ways food growers can save our soil through conservation. ___shelter belt___ ___contour plowing, terracing___

5. Which form of soil conservation would be suited for:
   a large area of windy, level, open plains? ___shelter belt terr___

   holding water for growing rice on the side of a hill? ___terracing___

6. Why is it essential that soil conservation be practiced throughout the world? ___because___ ___erosion would otherwise destroy soil needed to grow crops.___

A Last Look—Part I

A. In each of the following groups one item does not belong. Circle that item and in the space provided explain why it does not belong.

1.　　Krakatoa　　　　　　Mauna Loa　　　　　Appalachians

_____

2.　　　slate　　　　　　　　basalt　　　　　　　marble

_____

3.　　　crater　　　　　　　　scarp　　　　　　　fault surface

_____

4.　　hot spring　　　　　　gneiss　　　　　　　geyser

_____

5.　wide flood plain　　　steep valley　　　rapidly flowing water

_____

6.　　terracing　　　　contour plowing　　　streak testing

_____

7.　　galena　　　　　　　mantle　　　　　　　crust

_____

8.　　column　　　　　　　　sill　　　　　　　stalagmite

_____

9.　orthorhombic　　　　tetragonal　　　　　syncline

_____

10.　　shale　　　　　　　granite　　　　　　limestone

_____

B. Write the word that will make each sentence a true statement.

1. A block mountain with one steep face and one gently sloping side is a _____ type.

2. The process of breaking rocks into smaller pieces is called _____.

3. Strip cropping and contour plowing are methods of _____.

4. Wide flood plains are characteristic of stream valleys in the _____ stage.

5. The _____ is the thickest layer of the earth's interior.

6. Sudden movements of rock layers beneath the surface cause vibrations called _____.

7. When the roof of a cave collapses, a _____ is formed.

8. A major volcano and earthquake area encircles the _____ Ocean.

9. When hot molten rock called magma reaches the surface, it is called _____.

10. When a stalactite and a stalagmite are joined, a _____ is formed.

　　　　　Geology—Rocks and Minerals　I

A Last Look—Part II

A. On line **a,** name the rock shown.
On line **b,** tell if the rock is igneous, sedimentary, or metamorphic.

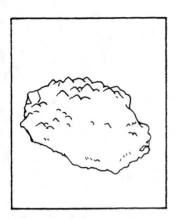

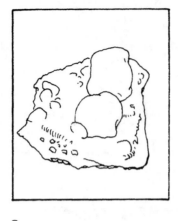

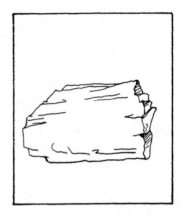

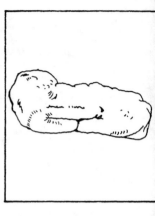

1. a. _____

    b. _____

2. a. _____

    b. _____

3. a. _____

    b. _____

4. a. _____

    b. _____

B. On the line below each picture, write the name of the geological feature shown.

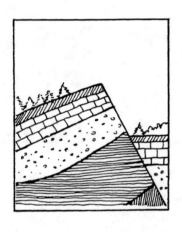

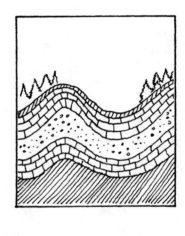

1. _____

2. _____

3. _____

4. _____

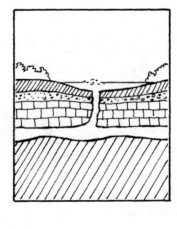

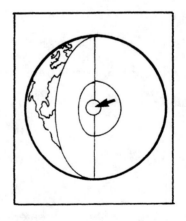

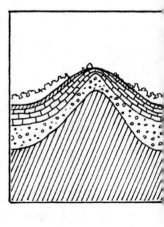

5. _____

6. _____

7. _____

8. _____

A Last Look—Part III

A. Find the statement in the second column that best describes each word in the first column. Write the letter of the statement before the word it describes.

1. _____ erosion
2. _____ metamorphic
3. _____ stalagmite
4. _____ crust
5. _____ sedimentary
6. _____ ore
7. _____ igneous
8. _____ Kilauea
9. _____ core
10. _____ stalactite

a. material that can be mined at a profit
b. geyser
c. rocks formed when magma cools and solidifies
d. a deposit formed on the roof of a cave
e. hottest layer of the earth
f. rocks changed deep in the earth by pressure and heat
g. volcano
h. a deposit formed on the floor of a cave
i. rocks formed from layers compressed under water
j. hardness test
k. continuous wearing away of land
l. outer layer of the earth

B. Circle the word (words) that will make each sentence a true statement.

1. The hardest mineral is _____ .

    talc   quartz   diamond

2. A _____ is a fracture line in rock strata.

    fold   fault   scarp

3. Limestone is _____ rock.

    an igneous   a metamorphic   a sedimentary

4. The temperature of rocks near the inner core of the earth is _____ the temperature of rocks near the crust.

    greater than   less than   the same as

5. Obsidian is _____ rock.

    an igneous   a metamorphic   a sedimentary

6. Steep cliffs called scarps are characteristic of _____ .

    folded mountains   block mountains   dome mountains

7. The softest mineral is _____ .

    talc   quartz   diamond

8. Marble is _____ rock that was originally limestone.

    an igneous   a metamorphic   a sedimentary

9. Ice, water, and wind are the major agents of _____ .

    mineral identification   erosion   ore extraction

10. The opening of a volcano is called the _____ .

    crater   dike   vent

A Last Look—Part IV

A. Explain fully the meaning of this cartoon.

"It's amazing what a little wind can do!"

_____

_____

_____

_____

B. There is something wrong with each of these drawings. Circle the part of the drawing that is incorrect and explain why you circled it.

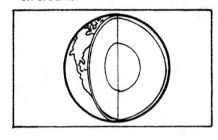

1. _____   2. _____

_____   _____

3. _____   4. _____

_____   _____

C. The names of all the rocks and minerals listed are hidden in the square of letters. See if you can find them all.

```
A N D A N T H R A C I T E I E S
B C R T U R Q U O I S E V O H G
E A O U L I M E S T O N E B T A
E L G N E I S S H A L L G S J L
L C P I G R F H L A P Y R I T E
W I C O S L A E T A P P A D O N
O T F I L D O S L A T Y N I Z A
L E G O N E J M M D I E I A I D
I X Y S W N O A E A S Y T N R C
V Z O O H A A R T R O P E U C A
I Q G R T A B B E E A M A N O P
N A Y I K U L L A H J T G R N A
E R P U M I C E J R W O E X I T
N U S A N D S T O N E P I E H I
D S U L F U R P K V B A S A L T
O P M L P D Q U A R T Z O U C E
```

anthracite	marble
apatite	obsidian
basalt	olivine
calcite	pumice
cinnabar	pyrite
conglomerate	quartz
feldspar	sandstone
galena	shale
gneiss	slate
granite	sulfur
gypsum	topaz
limestone	turquoise
	zircon

TRANSPARENCY SECTION

(Use the transparencies to
introduce each lesson.)